MINIONS™

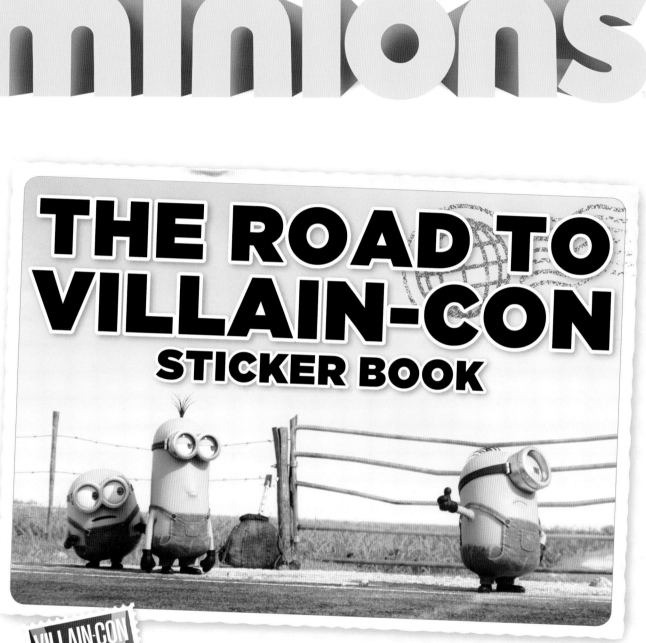

THE ROAD TO VILLAIN-CON
STICKER BOOK

VILLAIN-CON
INTERNATIONAL

By Trey King

centum

If you want to travel in style, you have to look the part. Pick your favourite outfit!

TOO MUCH TV? NEVER!

Kevin, Stuart, and Bob settle in for an evening of watching television. They pick up some weird channels after Stuart rigs a powerful antenna. What other shows might the Minions find?

TIME TO TRAVEL

You have a long way to go to get to Villain-Con, but don't worry! The Minions are experienced travellers and have some fun ideas about how to get there. Use the stickers to show your favourite ways to travel!

#1

#2

#3

TIC-TAC-MINION!

When the Minions get into the car with the Nelson family, they don't know what to do. If they played a game of tic-tac-toe, who do you think would win? Why don't you play and find out?

FANCY DRESS

BEST DRESSED

MOST FUN SWIMWEAR

VILLAIN-CON INTERNATIONAL

PROFESSOR FLUX
AHEAD OF OUR TIME SINCE 1945

Wish You Were Here!

Welcome to

Greetings from

NEW YORK

LONDON

ORLANDO

VILLAIN-CON INTERNATIONAL

HAND OUT THOSE CARDS!

UNIQUE

You made it to Villain-Con! Time to meet some bad guys. But first, make your business cards by adding your name and Minion stickers to each card!

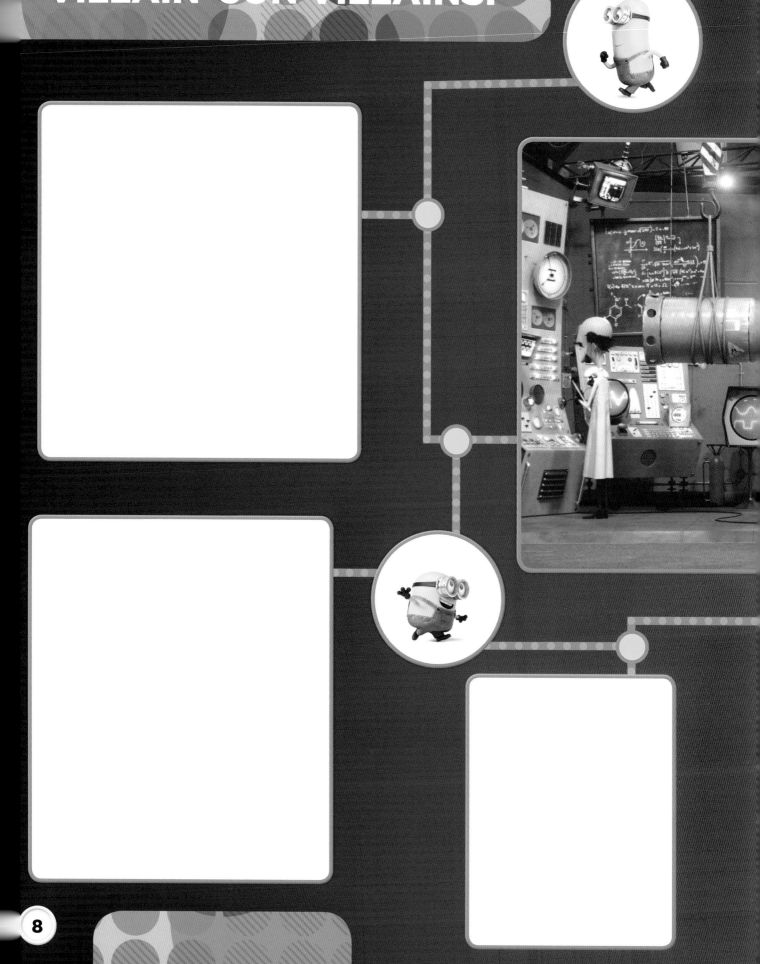

There are so many cool villains. Who will the Minions choose as their new master? Use your stickers to help the Minions meet the bad guys.

IT'S THAT TIME OF YEAR AGAIN
VILLAIN-CON
INTERNATIONAL

PROFESSOR
FLUX

HEAD OF OUR TIME
SINCE 1945

GET THAT RUBY!

Win a job as Scarlet Overkill's henchman! All you have to do is walk, run, sing or blast your way through the other job candidates and take the ruby. Good luck!

POSTCARDS!

PLACE STAMP HERE

PLACE STAMP HERE

1ST

1ST

You and the Minions managed to defeat the other villains and get the ruby! Now that you've proven yourselves worthy, Scarlet is taking you to her castle in London! Send postcards to your Minion tribe back home.